Anne of
Green Gables

Based on the Novel by Lucy Maude Montgomery
Adapted by Elizabeth West

SCHOLASTIC INC.

New York   Toronto   London   Auckland   Sydney
Mexico City   New Delhi   Hong Kong   Buenos Aires

Illustrations
Glin Dibley

Text copyright © 2003 by Scholastic Inc.
Illustrations copyright © 2003 by Glin Dibley.
All rights reserved. Published by Scholastic Inc.
Printed in the U.S.A.

ISBN 0-439-59768-4

10 11 12 13 14   23   14 15 16 17 18

Contents

Welcome to This Book

Have you ever been the new kid in town? Have you ever had trouble fitting in? Anne Shirley had those problems in a big way.

Anne wasn't a bad kid. She was just different. She did things that other kids didn't. Once Anne sailed away in a leaky boat and almost drowned. She looked different, too. Her red hair was as wild as her ideas.

Would Anne ever figure out how to fit in? Or would people learn to accept her and her shocking ways?

Target Words These words will help you get to know Anne a little better.

- **orphan:** a child who has no parents
  Anne is an orphan.

- **proper:** having formal manners
  Anne's ways are a little wild and not at all proper.

- **romantic:** a dreamy view of life
  Anne wants everything to be romantic and special.

Reader Tips Here's how to get the most out of this book.

- **Meet the Characters** Check out the characters on pages 6–7. Connect their names with their pictures as you read.

- **Analyze the Characters** Think about how Anne and the other characters are described. Watch for what they think, say, and do.

Meet the Characters

This story is set in the early 1900s on a small island in Canada. The name of the island is Avonlea. This list will help you keep the characters straight.

Anne Shirley
An 11-year-old orphan. She is sent to Avonlea where she hopes to find a real home.

Matthew Cuthbert
A 60-year-old farmer. He lives at Green Gables. He is getting older and needs help on the farm.

Marilla Cuthbert
Matthew's sister. She is a little younger than he is. She lives with him at Green Gables. The two decide to get an orphan to help with the work.

Diana Barry
Mrs. Barry's daughter. She is the same age as Anne.

Gilbert Blythe
A handsome boy in Anne's class. He loves to tease Anne.

Matthew picks up Anne from the train station.

CHAPTER

1

The Wrong Orphan

***Anne has always wanted to be part of a family.
But what if they don't want her?***

Matthew got to the train station a little late.
Their **orphan** would be waiting! Matthew and
his sister wanted a boy who could help with the
chores. Matthew certainly needed help. He was
getting old.

However, he didn't see any boy at the station.

"You must be Matthew Cuthbert," said a girl
in an ugly, yellow dress. "I'm your orphan."

Matthew didn't know what to say. Someone
had made a mistake!

"I've been waiting," she said. "I was afraid
you weren't coming."

Matthew was a shy man. He wasn't used to
girls. What should he do now? He couldn't leave
this girl alone at the station. He'd better take

her home. Then his sister could decide what to do. He hoped things would work out.

Matthew didn't say much. The girl didn't notice. And she talked a lot. "Look at all the beautiful flowers! I've always heard about the flowers in Avonlea. What's that pond called?"

"That's the Barrys' pond," said Matthew.

"I'll call it Shining Waters," she said cheerfully. "That sounds more **romantic**. Does Green **Gables** have a pond? Then I'd be truly happy. Well, sort of happy. I'd be truly happy with dark hair. I hate my red hair."

The girl saw a small house in the distance and pointed to it. "Is that Green Gables?"

Matthew nodded.

"This will be my first real home," she said. "It's perfect!"

⌐Heads Up!⌐

What is Anne like? Think of two words that describe her.

2

Marilla Decides

Will Marilla let Anne stay?

Marilla pointed at the girl. "Who's that?" she asked. "And where's our boy?"

"There was only her," said Matthew. He didn't even know the girl's name.

"We asked for a boy," said Marilla sharply.

The girl started to cry. "You don't want me!" she sobbed. "Nobody wants me! Are you going to send me back?"

"No," said Marilla. "We'll take care of this tomorrow. What's your name?"

"Anne Shirley, " said the girl. "That's Anne with an *e*. That's better than just plain Ann."

Marilla led Anne to a small bedroom. The girl undressed and crawled into bed.

"Good night," said Marilla.

"It's not good," said Anne. "It's my worst night ever!" Then Anne pulled the covers over her face.

Marilla went downstairs. She found Matthew deep in thought.

"She really is a nice little thing," he said.

"Don't grow attached to her," said Marilla.

The next morning Anne came into the kitchen and looked outside. "The trees and flowers are calling me," she said sadly. "But I'm leaving. I don't want to fall in love with them."

"We'll see," Marilla said.

Marilla and Anne drove back toward the station in their **buggy.** At first Anne looked quite sad. Then she smiled.

"I might as well enjoy this beautiful day," she said.

"Tell me about yourself," said Marilla.

"I'm eleven," said Anne. "My parents died long ago. Only Mrs. Thomas would take me. She'd been our cleaning lady. I helped take care of her children. But then she had to move."

Marilla listened quietly to Anne.

"Later a neighbor woman took me in. She had eight children. I took care of them too. But then her husband died. So she sent her children to live with relatives. After that, I had nowhere to go," Anne told her.

When Anne had finished, Marilla said softly, "Were these women good to you?"

"They tried," said Anne, after a moment.

Marilla looked at Anne's pale, thin face. She felt sorry for the girl. "Matthew wants you to stay," she said slowly.

Anne's eyes sparkled. "Really?" she said. "Can I stay at Green Gables?"

"Yes," said Marilla. And then she turned the buggy around.

Matthew heard the buggy and came outside. When he saw Anne, he smiled.

—Heads Up!—

Why do you think Marilla changes her mind about keeping Anne?

3

Anne Learns a Lesson

Anne shocks everyone at church.

Anne said, "May I call you Aunt Marilla? We could **imagine** you're my real aunt."

Marilla said, "I couldn't. Just call me Marilla."

"Don't you imagine things?" asked Anne.

"No," said Marilla. "Get ready for church."

"Maybe I'll make a friend there," said Anne. "I've always wanted a best friend."

"Diana Barry lives nearby," said Marilla. "Maybe she'll be your friend. She's very nice."

"I hope she doesn't have red hair," said Anne. "I think red hair's ugly."

"Diana's good and smart," said Marilla. "That's better than being beautiful."

Marilla had bought Anne three dresses. Anne thought they were all very plain. She didn't like any of them. But after a while, she forced herself to choose one. I'll just imagine it's fancy, she thought to herself.

"I can't come to church today," said Marilla. "Try and behave yourself."

On the way to church, Anne saw beautiful wildflowers. She picked them and put them around her hat. "That's better," she thought. Then she raced off to church. When she got there, everyone stared. But Anne did not notice.

"What were you thinking? No one puts weeds on their hats. That's just silly, Anne!" Marilla said when she heard about it later.

"It isn't silly!" Anne said. Then she burst into tears. "Now you're angry with me. Please don't send me away!"

"I won't," said Marilla. "But I do wish you'd learn to act a bit more **proper**."

Heads Up!

Look up the word proper *in the glossary. Give an example of acting proper.*

Anne puts beautiful wildflowers on her hat.

4

Best Friends

**_Anne meets Diana Barry. Will she become
Anne's new best friend?_**

The next day Marilla and Anne walked to
the Barrys to pay a visit.

"Watch your manners!" Marilla warned.
"Mrs. Barry is very strict about Diana's friends."

Anne trembled. "What if Mrs. Barry doesn't
like me?"

"Then she won't let you see Diana," said
Marilla as she knocked at the door.

Mrs. Barry opened the door herself. "Is this
your orphan?" she asked.

"Yes. This is Anne Shirley," said Marilla.

"That's Anne with an _e_!" added Anne.

Mrs. Barry looked surprised. But Anne didn't
notice. Behind Mrs. Barry was a young girl.
Anne knew it must be Diana. How pretty Diana

was! She had dark curly hair and pink cheeks.

"Take Anne outside and show her your flowers," said Mrs. Barry.

The two girls walked into a beautiful garden. Anne felt happy.

Finally, she said, "Could you ever like me a little? Could you ever be my friend?"

Diana laughed. "I guess so. I sure am glad you've moved in. There was no one for miles."

"Will you swear to be my friend forever?" asked Anne.

Diana looked shocked. "Isn't swearing **wicked?**" she said.

"Not that kind of swearing," said Anne. "I just want you to promise."

"OK," said Diana. "I promise. We'll be friends forever."

Heads Up!

Think of the words you picked to decribe Anne. Now think of a word that describes Diana. How are these girls different?

5

Anne Gets in Trouble

Anne meets Gilbert for the first time.

One day at school, Diana pointed out Gilbert Blythe. He sat in a row across from Anne.

"He's been away visiting his cousins for the last few months," said Diana. "He's so handsome! But he's a big tease."

Anne watched him tease some other girl. He tacked her braids to the chair.

"What terrible manners!" thought Anne.

Later he tried to catch Anne's attention. But she was daydreaming. He tried again without luck. Then he tugged one of Anne's braids.

"Carrots! Carrots!" he yelled. "Your hair's the color of carrots!"

Anne jumped to her feet and shouted, "You are a mean, hateful boy!"

Anne smacks Gilbert on the head with her slate.

Then she smacked Gilbert on the head with her **slate**.

The teacher was very angry. To punish Anne, he made her stand in the corner. Gilbert tried to explain that it was all his fault. But the teacher wouldn't listen.

Later Gilbert told Anne he was sorry. He even gave her a little candy heart. But Anne tossed it on the floor and crushed it.

—**Heads Up!**—

Why do you think Anne gets so mad at Gilbert? Think about what she said in Chapter 1 about red hair.

6

A Wicked Girl

Will Anne lose her best friend?

The next day Anne said she would not go back to school. Marilla did not make her go. She knew that Anne would change her mind.

Anne was becoming more responsible at home. So one day Marilla planned a trip to town.

"May I invite Diana over for tea?" asked Anne. "I miss her."

Marilla said, "Yes. You may even serve some of our raspberry juice."

Anne was thrilled. What a treat! This juice was served only to special guests. Anne sent a note inviting Diana.

Both girls wore their fanciest dresses. Anne served the raspberry juice and told funny stories about herself. Diana listened happily and drank her juice.

Anne was too busy talking to drink. But Diana had a second glass of juice. Then, she had a third.

Suddenly she said, "I…I don't feel very well. I want to go home." She stood up unsteadily.

"Please stay!" said Anne. But Diana shook her head and rushed out.

The next day, Anne heard that Mrs. Barry was very angry. Diana had come home drunk!

Marilla was stunned. "What did you serve Diana?" she asked. Anne showed her the bottle.

Marilla said, "That's not juice, Anne! It's wine! I moved the juice to the cupboard!"

Both Anne and Marilla tried to explain the mistake. But Mrs. Barry wouldn't listen.

"That Anne is a wicked girl! She did this on purpose," she told Diana. "You may never visit her again!"

Heads Up!

Do you agree with what Mrs. Barry says about Anne? Do you think she is being fair?

7

Anne to the Rescue

Diana's little sister becomes very ill. Can Anne help?

Anne cried to Marilla, "It's all over. I'll never have another friend. In fact, I'll probably die soon. Perhaps Mrs. Barry will feel sorry then!"

Marilla shook her head. Anne would get over her sorrow in time. She was so **dramatic**.

Sure enough, Anne cheered up quickly. She had a new plan. She would go back to school. At least she could see Diana there.

Everyone greeted her happily. One boy gave her a pencil. Anne smiled warmly at him. Gilbert tried to give her an apple. But Anne turned away.

One January night, an important man was giving a speech nearby. Many of the adults went to hear him. Marilla and Mrs. Barry were among them. Matthew stayed home with Anne.

Later that night, Anne heard a pounding on her door. She ran to open it. Diana stood there. She looked scared to death.

"Minnie May's got croup," she said. "She's really sick. There's no one home but me. I don't know what to do!"

"Don't worry," said Anne. "I've taken care of lots of children. I've seen plenty of croup."

She followed Diana home. Matthew hurried to get a doctor.

Little Minnie May looked deathly sick. Her breathing made a harsh sound.

"Boil some water!" shouted Anne. "Bring some blankets!" Minnie May lay white-faced on her bed. Anne wrapped the child in blankets. She had Minnie May breathe in the warm steam.

—Heads Up!—

When children get sick with croup, they have trouble breathing. They cough a lot. Breathing steamy air helps.

Anne helps Minne May feel better.

Diana stood by, frozen with fear. Helpless tears rolled down her face.

Anne took care of Minnie May for hours. At last the child's breathing sounded better. Everyone gave a sigh of relief.

The doctor arrived several hours later and took over.

The next day, he told Mrs. Barry, "That little red-headed girl saved your child's life! I never saw anything like it!"

Mrs. Barry apologized to Anne. "I can never thank you enough," she said. "I hope you'll be Diana's friend again."

8

A Very Bad Hair Day

There are some things worse than red hair.

Time passed quickly at Avonlea. The teacher left, and a new teacher arrived. Her name was Miss Muriel Stacy. "What a romantic name!" thought Anne.

Anne liked Miss Stacy a lot. She encouraged Anne. She made Anne feel special. Anne wanted to do her very best for Miss Stacy. School was becoming important to her.

One evening Marilla came home with a bad headache. She was looking forward to sitting by a warm fire. But when she got home, there was no fire and no Anne. Why had Anne not done her chores? Making the fire was the girl's job. Marilla waited.

Finally, Marilla went upstairs to check Anne's room. To Marilla's surprise, the girl was in there. She could hear Anne sobbing through the door.

"Don't come in!" she cried.

"Are you sick?" asked Marilla.

"No. Please go away," said Anne. "Don't look at me."

"What's the matter, Anne?" said Marilla. She walked into the room with her candle.

"My goodness!" exclaimed Marilla. "What happened to your hair?"

"I hated my red hair. So I decided to dye it. I used black dye. But it turned my hair green." She sounded miserable.

Marilla said, "See where **vanity** got you?"

Anne couldn't wash out the dye. Finally, she handed Marilla some scissors.

─Heads Up!──────────────

Look up vanity *in the glossary. Think about what vanity means to you. What's an example of someone being vain?*

"Just cut if off," she said. "I'll look at it every single day. That will remind me of my vanity. I'd like to be beautiful. But you're right. It's better to be good."

Anne asks Marilla to cut off her hair.

9

A Romantic Adventure

Anne's adventure goes very wrong.

Anne was fourteen now. She and her friends often studied together after school. One day they were studying a romantic poem. They decided to act it out.

One person in the poem was supposed to float down a river in a boat. None of the other girls would play her part. They were all too scared. Anne became **impatient.**

"I'll do it!" Anne said. "Give me that black shawl. And hand me a bunch of flowers."

Anne lay down inside the boat. The boat began to drift slowly down the river.

"Isn't this romantic!" thought Anne. But then water began leaking into the boat. The boat started to sink. Anne was cold and wet. That wasn't romantic at all!

Anne's boat is sinking fast.

Anne sat up. She saw a bridge up ahead of her. She hoped that the boat would reach it in time. But the boat was sinking fast. Muddy water already covered her feet.

The boat sank right underneath the bridge. Luckily, Anne was able to grab a bridge post and hang from it. She gripped it with all her might. She clung there for a long time.

"Anne Shirley! What on earth are you doing up there?"

Anne looked down. Gilbert Blythe had been out rowing on the river. He helped her climb down into his boat.

Anne was safe. But now she had to explain what happened. Gilbert listened and didn't laugh. He didn't want to give Anne another reason to be mad at him.

"Can't we be friends?" he said. "I'm sorry I teased you. Anyway, that was years ago."

Gilbert held his breath and waited for Anne's answer. He even crossed his fingers. He wanted Anne to forgive him. He hoped they could finally be friends.

Anne **hesitated**. She looked at Gilbert's face. He was smiling at her. Her heart gave a quick little beat. She wanted to say yes. It was on the tip of her tongue. But she couldn't forget how Gilbert had called her "carrots."

Coldly, she said, "Never!"

Later she told Marilla, "Every mistake has taught me something. I've learned not to be careless or vain. Today I learned not to be too romantic."

─Heads Up!──────────────

Anne wants life to be romantic like a poem. But is it? Why or why not?

10

An Old Enemy

Will Anne ever forgive Gilbert?

One night Marilla sat looking at Anne. She had really grown to love that girl like her own child. She knew that the time had come for Anne to plan for her future.

"Anne," she said, "Mrs. Stacy was here today. She's starting a class for her best students. She wants you to join. She says that you could go to college. She says you could be a teacher."

Anne was delighted. She went to this new class very happy. Then she saw her old enemy, Gilbert Blythe, sitting there.

Anne was determined not to notice him. He was just as determined not to notice her. She wasn't really angry at him anymore. But she didn't know how to change things.

Anne studied hard for two months. Then she took the tests to get into college. She hoped to make Marilla and Matthew proud. She also hoped to earn a higher score than Gilbert. But she wouldn't learn the test results for weeks.

Anne spent the summer pleasantly. But two things made her a bit sad. Diana wasn't going to college. She would remain in Avonlea. Also, Marilla and Matthew weren't very healthy. Marilla often had headaches. Matthew had problems with his heart.

Late in the summer, Anne saw Diana racing down the path toward her. Diana was waving the newspaper. "Anne! Anne!" she cried. "You passed! You're in first place! You and Gilbert are tied for first place!"

That meant that Anne was going away to college! But, so was Gilbert.

At college, Anne was actually glad to see Gilbert. He reminded her of home. Also, she enjoyed their **rivalry**. She worked extra hard to beat him in every subject. And her hard work paid off with an award.

This award would pay for another two years of college. This was great because Anne wanted to keep going. But Gilbert was headed back home. His family couldn't afford to pay for any more college. Instead, Gilbert would return to Avonlea to teach. For the first time, Anne realized she would miss Gilbert.

During summer vacation, Anne returned to Green Gables. She was looking forward to seeing Gilbert and her family. But when she got there, she became worried. Neither Matthew nor Marilla looked well.

Then one day Matthew got a letter from the bank. The bank had gone out of business. The family's savings were all gone. He got so upset that he collapsed and died on the spot. But that wasn't all. Soon after, Marilla learned she was going blind. How could she keep Green Gables all alone, with no money and no sight?

"Don't worry," Anne told Marilla. "You'll never lose Green Gables. You took care of me. Now it's my turn to help you. I won't go back to college. I'll get a teaching job somewhere nearby."

Anne and Gilbert have a lot to talk about.

Gilbert had already gotten the job at Avonlea. So she'd find one a little farther away.

A few days later, Anne received surprising news. The teaching job in Avonlea was available after all. Gilbert had turned it down. He asked the school board to offer it to Anne.

The next time Anne saw Gilbert, she held out her hand. "Thank you," she said. "I really appreciate your kindness."

Gilbert didn't let go of her hand right away. Anne blushed. She liked holding hands with Gilbert. Then Gilbert broke the silence.

"You're welcome," he said. "Does this mean you've forgiven me? After all this time, are we finally going to be friends?"

Anne laughed. "I forgave you years ago," she said, blushing some more. "I just couldn't admit it. And I've been sorry ever since."

"Let me walk home with you," said Gilbert happily. "We have a lot of catching up to do."

So, Anne and Gilbert walked back to Green Gables to tell Marilla the good news. They held hands the whole way.

Glossary

buggy *(noun)* small carriage pulled by a horse (p. 12)

dramatic *(adjective)* making a big fuss (p. 24)

gable *(noun)* part of a roof that sticks out and is shaped like a triangle (p. 10)

hesitate *(verb)* to pause (p. 34)

imagine *(verb)* to pretend (p. 14)

impatient *(adjective)* easily annoyed (p. 31)

orphan *(noun)* a child who has no parents (p. 9)

proper *(adjective)* having formal manners (p. 15)

rivalry *(noun)* a competition or contest (p. 36)

romantic *(adjective)* a dreamy view of life (p. 10)

slate *(noun)* a smooth stone to write on (p. 21)

vanity *(noun)* being too worried about how you look (p. 29)

wicked *(adjective)* it used to mean badly behaved; now it means really bad or evil. (p. 18)